Think → Write → Share

JN089241

Advanced 1

Three Reasons

Read and write about a choice
Think of three good reasons about the topic and write about it

TAGAKI Advanced 1 gives ample practice to Think --> Write --> Share about choices you make. There are many choices to be made in life, from small to large, and people all over the world make choices all the time in everyday life.

What choice would you make about the 30 topics in this workbook? Why would you choose that? Let's look deeply into it. When you do that, and you get into the habit of coming up with three reasons for why you made a choice, it will help you increase your ability to express yourself. Let's talk about the choices you make, with humor. Let's think, write and share in English.

TAGAKI Advanced 1
Three Reasons

Contents

 **TAGAKI Advanced 1** Three Reasons

1 Reading and Listening Time

Read the sample sentences about topic A. Listen to the audio.

Please note that the audio recording of this book contains pronunciations of some words as commonly spoken by users of American English.

Useful Expressions
Use some of the useful expressions, if you like.

1 Apartments or Houses

A **B**

Sample Sentences

Apartments

Lead Apartments are better than houses for three reasons.

Reason 1 First, apartments are smaller than houses. They are just right for people who do not want to spend all day cleaning.

Reason 2 Second, if something breaks down in your rental apartment, do not worry! The landlord will fix or replace it.

Reason 3 Lastly, it is easy to make friends with your neighbors in an apartment building. They will often greet you when you get back home from work or school. They will even greet your dog!

 My Opinion

Actually, I prefer living in a house. I feel free to do whatever I like in my own house. Once, we painted the bedroom yellow, the living room blue, and the kitchen red! I am not kidding! It was beautiful!

How to write your own version

Lead Start your essay with the lead sentence.

Reason 1
Reason 2 Write reason 1/2/3 for topic B.
Reason 3

My Opinion
Write your own opinion about the topic you want to choose, A or B.

2 Thinking Time

Think of three good points about topic B.

3 Writing Time ❶

Using the structure of the sample sentences, write more than 70 words.
Use some of the useful expressions, if you like.

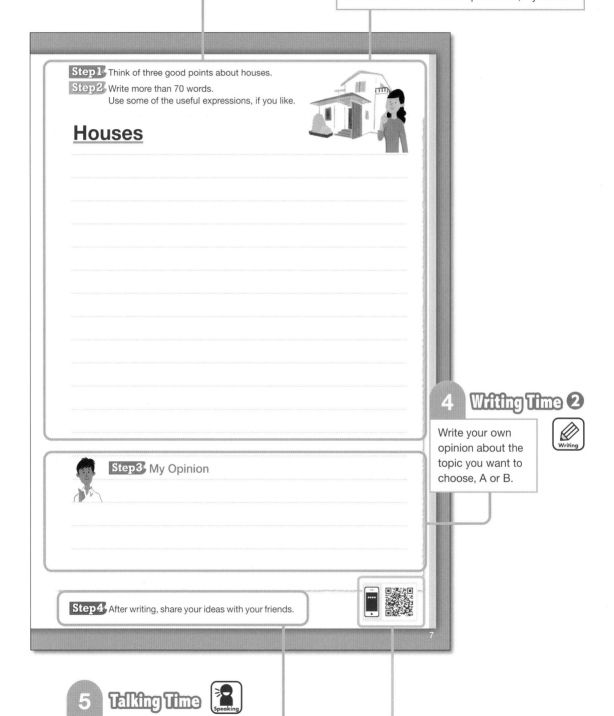

Step1 Think of three good points about houses.
Step2 Write more than 70 words.
Use some of the useful expressions, if you like.

Houses

4 Writing Time ❷

Write your own opinion about the topic you want to choose, A or B.

Step3 My Opinion

Step4 After writing, share your ideas with your friends.

5 Talking Time

Present what you wrote by reading it out loud, or even better, memorize it, then present it.

Listen to the sample sentences the way they are spoken with contractions.

5

1 Apartments or Houses

Sample Sentences

Apartments

 Apartments are better than houses for three reasons.

 First, apartments are smaller than houses. They are just right for people who do not want to spend all day cleaning.

 Second, if something breaks down in your rental apartment, do not worry! The landlord will fix or replace it.

 Lastly, it is easy to make friends with your neighbors in an apartment building. They will often greet you when you get back home from work or school. They will even greet your dog!

 My Opinion

Actually, I prefer living in a house. I feel free to do whatever I like in my own house. Once, we painted the bedroom yellow, the living room blue, and the kitchen red! I am not kidding! It was beautiful!

Step 1 Think of three good points about houses.

Step 2 Write more than 70 words.
Use some of the useful expressions, if you like.

Houses

 Step 3 My Opinion

Step 4 After writing, share your ideas with your friends.

2 Cash or Cashless

Cash

 Using cash is better than going cashless. Here is why.

 With cash, you can see exactly how much money you have. You can think, "Wow! I am rich!"

 Using cash is simple. If you lose your wallet, that is bad, but at least you do not have to worry about canceling your cards.

 When you travel abroad, it is really fun to use foreign bills and coins, especially the ones with different sizes, colors, and cultural designs.

 My Opinion

Credit cards are just plastic. Online payments are just numbers. I like cash because I can see, touch, and even smell my money. My piggy bank thinks it is delicious, too!

Step 1 Think of three good points about going cashless.

Step 2 Write more than 70 words.
Use some of the useful expressions, if you like.

Cashless

 Step 3 My Opinion

Step 4 After writing, share your ideas with your friends.

 # Cold Countries or Hot Countries

  ## Cold Countries

Lead Cold countries are better than hot countries because …

Reason 1 You can enjoy cold countries all year round. In summer, you can go hiking or sightseeing. In winter, you can ski or have a snowball fight!

Reason 2 On a snowy evening, you can sit in front of a cozy fire and drink hot chocolate.

Reason 3 People seldom care about their body type in cold countries. After all, everyone looks the same when they stay warm under big sweaters or jackets!

 ### My Opinion

The truth is, I like hot countries better. I would rather lie on a beach with a cold drink and work on my suntan. That is more relaxing than trying to stay warm in a cold country.

Hot Countries

Step 3 My Opinion

Step 4 After writing, share your ideas with your friends.

11

4 **Country Life** or **City Life**

  ## Country Life

 Why country life is better than city life.

 Country life is less stressful. It is quiet and peaceful. You can make friends with easygoing people, and wild animals, too!

 It is also true that it is a healthier lifestyle. You spend more time in the sunshine and fresh air and eat vegetables from your own garden.

 You can keep interesting pets. Instead of just goldfish, cats, or dogs, you can also keep chickens, goats, or alpacas!

 My Opinion

I also prefer to live in the country. When I go to sleep, I do not hear trains, buses, or cars running, but birds, crickets, and frogs singing. And instead of waking up to a noisy alarm clock, I hear a friendly rooster calling out, "Cock-a-doodle-doo!"

12

City Life

Step 3 My Opinion

Cycling or Running

Sample Sentences

Cycling

Lead Why cycling may be better than running.

Reason 1 You can imagine yourself as a superhero when you ride a bicycle. You happily fly past everyone. Even barking dogs!

Reason 2 The fact is, you can travel farther on a bicycle than on foot. You can see more things and meet more people.

Reason 3 You can carry things on your bicycle. That is a big advantage. You can take a small tent, your sleeping bag, and a cooking pot. And most importantly, snacks!

My Opinion

I really prefer cycling to running. Cycling is both fun and good exercise. Running? That is just hard work. It is not for me.

Step 1 Think of three good points about running.

Step 2 Write more than 70 words.
Use some of the useful expressions, if you like.

<u>Running</u>

Step 3 My Opinion

Step 4 After writing, share your ideas with your friends.

Digital Books or Paper Books

Digital Books

 Why I think digital books are better than paper books.

 Digital books are so convenient! For one thing, you can take a digital book anywhere. Not only that, you can read it in the dark.

 You can download as many digital books as you like. This saves space because you do not need to keep them on a shelf.

 With online audio books, writers often read their own books. Hearing their real voices can make you feel a stronger connection to the writers.

 My Opinion

Maybe I am old fashioned, but I actually prefer reading paper books. I like to read in bed with my head on my pillow and my book gently covering my face as I fall asleep. "Zzzzzzzz ..."

Step 1 Think of three good points about paper books.

Step 2 Write more than 70 words.
Use some of the useful expressions, if you like.

<u>Paper Books</u>

Step 3 My Opinion

Step 4 After writing, share your ideas with your friends.

7 Entrepreneurs or Artists

Entrepreneurs

Lead It is better to be an entrepreneur than an artist for three reasons.

Reason 1 For one thing, you can be your own boss. Nobody tells you what to do.

Reason 2 We can see that entrepreneurs can make big money! They start small companies and earn some money. They sell the companies and earn more money. As their companies grow, they turn good ideas into gold.

Reason 3 Entrepreneurs can take pride in their work because they change the world. They do this with courage and persistence. They are not afraid of anything and they never give up. Be a risk taker. Be a hero. Be an entrepreneur!

My Opinion

Actually, I would rather be a rich and famous artist. Musicians, painters, writers, designers, and actors all make the world happy. Making money at the same time would be a dream come true!

Step 1 Think of three good points about artists.

Step 2 Write more than 70 words.
Use some of the useful expressions, if you like.

Artists

Step 3 My Opinion

Step 4 After writing, share your ideas with your friends.

 **Family Trips** or **School Trips**

  # Family Trips

 Family trips are better than school trips. Here is why.

 If you ask me, without school rules, you can relax more. Your parents can, too. On a family trip, everybody is usually in a good mood.

 As for family activities, they are just fun! No assignments. No listening to lectures, taking notes, or writing essays.

 You can get to know your family members better, too. You make memories together to take back to your "home, sweet home."

 My Opinion

I love family trips, too. Everybody in my family is always busy doing so many things, so our trips together are very special. We laugh and share jokes nobody else would understand.

Step 1 Think of three good points about school trips.

Step 2 Write more than 70 words.
Use some of the useful expressions, if you like.

School Trips

Step 3 My Opinion

Step 4 After writing, share your ideas with your friends.

 **Fingers** or **Chopsticks**

Fingers

 Eating with your fingers is better than eating with chopsticks because …

 People in many cultures eat with their fingers. They recommend it because food tastes better when you involve all five senses.

 Furthermore, they say that when you eat with your fingers, you eat more slowly. You feel full sooner, so you eat less.

 Have you ever burned your mouth with hot food? That does not happen when you eat with your fingers. Thanks to your fingers, your mouth will stay safe.

 My Opinion

I also like to eat with my fingers. I have even eaten curry and rice with my fingers. It was messy and my fingers smelled like curry for days, but I did not care. I really enjoyed that meal.

Step 1 Think of three good points about chopsticks.

Step 2 Write more than 70 words.
Use some of the useful expressions, if you like.

Chopsticks

Step 3 My Opinion

Step 4 After writing, share your ideas with your friends.

 # Free Clothes or School Uniforms

  # Free Clothes

 Lead Why I think wearing free clothes is better than wearing school uniforms.

 Reason 1 Students can express their personalities through their fashion choices. Be yourself! Even if you just wear a T-shirt and jeans, that is you!

 Reason 2 You can select clothes that best fit your style, body, and coloring. You look good, feel good, and can study better.

 Reason 3 Choosing your own clothes makes you think. At first, you might decide one thing, but then you might change your mind. You learn to make decisions.

 My Opinion

I never wore school uniforms and I do not think I would like them. How boring! Choosing clothes in the morning wakes up my brain. And my brain needs all the exercise it can get!

Step 1 Think of three good points about school uniforms.

Step 2 Write more than 70 words.
Use some of the useful expressions, if you like.

School Uniforms

Step 3 My Opinion

Step 4 After writing, share your ideas with your friends.

11 Home-cooked Food or Fast Food

Home-cooked Food

Lead Why I think home-cooked food is better than fast food.

Reason 1 Most of us agree that home-cooked food is healthier for you. It does not usually contain preservatives or chemicals. And you can control how much fat, salt, and sugar you use.

Reason 2 Home-cooked food tastes good, too, because flavors need time to blend well. Besides, while you are waiting for it to cook, the house smells so good!

Reason 3 Finally, you can get creative when you make home-cooked food. You can try new things. It is fun to exchange recipes with your friends, too.

My Opinion

Home-cooked food is better for me both physically and emotionally. It reminds me of home. It is comfort food. We will not find grandma's delicious dishes at a fast food restaurant!

Step 1 Think of three good points about fast food.

Step 2 Write more than 70 words.
Use some of the useful expressions, if you like.

Fast Food

Step 3 My Opinion

Step 4 After writing, share your ideas with your friends.

 Individual Sports or Team Sports

Individual Sports

 Why individual sports may be better than team sports.

 You can concentrate on your skills. Golfers hit the ball. Skiers go faster and faster. They do not think about anything else.

 You can learn how strong or how weak you are. The thing is, you cannot hide behind teammates. It is not "One for all, all for one." but, "Me for me!"

 You can play or practice alone anytime, day or night. For example, you can practice putting at 10:00 p.m. if you like.

 My Opinion

I prefer individual sports, too. I love playing golf or going bowling. Personally, I do not like to run and most team sports involve running. No thank you.

Step 1 Think of three good points about team sports.

Step 2 Write more than 70 words.
Use some of the useful expressions, if you like.

Team Sports

 Step 3 My Opinion

Step 4 After writing, share your ideas with your friends.

13 Living Pets or Robot Pets

Living Pets

 Lead Why I think living pets are better than robot pets.

 Reason 1 Let us start with the fact that living pets have feelings. And they sense your feelings, too. When you are sad, they comfort you. When you are happy, they dance with you!

 Reason 2 Living pets are wonderful. They are cute and fun to watch. They make us happy, especially when they lick our faces.

 Reason 3 Children can learn a lot from feeding and caring for living pets. They learn to be responsible.

 My Opinion
Nothing can truly replace a living pet. Several years ago, I had a cat named Buddy. He used to wake me up every morning and welcome me home every evening. Unfortunately, he got sick and died. I cried and cried for days! I still miss him.

Step 1 Think of three good points about robot pets.

Step 2 Write more than 70 words.
Use some of the useful expressions, if you like.

<u>Robot Pets</u>

Step 3 My Opinion

Step 4 After writing, share your ideas with your friends.

 # Making Phone Calls or Texting

  ## Making Phone Calls

 Lead Making phone calls is better than texting for three reasons.

 Reason 1 It is easy to talk on the phone. Talking back and forth is the most natural way to communicate.

 Reason 2 You can express your feelings more accurately through your voice. For example, the true meaning is different if you say "Oh!", compared to "Oh?", or "Ooooh …"

 Reason 3 Additionally, phone calls are faster. You can explain yourself more quickly and get answers right away.

 My Opinion

I also like phone calls. Texting gets me in trouble sometimes when I type something wrong by mistake. Maybe my fingers are just too fat. In any case, I like talking better than typing.

Step 1 Think of three good points about texting.

Step 2 Write more than 70 words.
Use some of the useful expressions, if you like.

Texting

Step 3 My Opinion

Step 4 After writing, share your ideas with your friends.

 **Night People** or **Morning People**

 Sample Sentences

Night People

Lead It is better to be a night person than a morning person. Here is why.

Reason 1 Night people like to have fun. They like to go to concerts, movies, or play games at night.

Reason 2 Some people say that night people are more romantic. They love the moon and stars. When they see a shooting star, they usually make a wish.

Reason 3 Night people can be very creative. A lot of artists, writers, or musicians seem to get their best ideas at night. There is no need to be scared of the dark.

 My Opinion

I am naturally a night person. While morning people are studying, doing exercise, and so on and so forth, I enjoy my late morning sleep. Actually, I do not really mind the morning itself. I just wish it came later in the day.

Step 1 Think of three good points about morning people.

Step 2 Write more than 70 words.
Use some of the useful expressions, if you like.

Morning People

Step 3 My Opinion

Step 4 After writing, share your ideas with your friends.

35

 # Online Schools or Regular Schools

  ## Online Schools

 Online schools are better than regular schools because …

 Your schedule is very flexible. You can study or take a break at your own pace. There are no school bells.

 Online schools are efficient. One reason is that you do not have to waste time, money, or energy on traveling. You can save your effort for your studies.

 You do not have to care about your looks. You can study with messy hair, in bare feet and pajamas.

 My Opinion

As for me, I would rather go to a regular school.
Studying online is too lonely. I am a people person.
I like talking to my friends and teachers in person. It is more enjoyable to eat lunch together, too.

Step 1 Think of three good points about regular schools.

Step 2 Write more than 70 words.
Use some of the useful expressions, if you like.

Regular Schools

Step 3 My Opinion

Step 4 After writing, share your ideas with your friends.

 **Physical Sports or Esports**

Physical Sports

Lead Why physical sports are better than esports.

Reason 1 In my opinion, playing physical sports is an excellent way to get some exercise. You sweat and enjoy a refreshing shower afterwards. And you can sleep very well.

Reason 2 Even though your muscles might get sore from physical sports, most people agree it feels good to use them. You will get stronger and maybe lose weight, too!

Reason 3 Many physical sports are played outside in the sunshine and fresh air. That is good for your health.

 My Opinion

I like physical sports, too. If you are shy, they are a great way to make new friends. In the beginning, you do not have to talk a lot, you just enjoy the game. After that, you look forward to meeting each other again.

Step 1 Think of three good points about esports.

Step 2 Write more than 70 words.
Use some of the useful expressions, if you like.

Esports

Step 3 My Opinion

Step 4 After writing, share your ideas with your friends.

18 Real Views or Pictures

Real Views

 Why real views may be better than pictures.

 I am confident that many people would agree real views are exciting to see.

Reason 2 For one thing, the scale is different. You really have no idea how magnificent Niagara Falls, the Grand Canyon, the Great Wall of China, or the Parthenon are, just from a photo.

 Furthermore, your experience will make a deeper impression on you and you will keep the memory forever.

My Opinion

Real views are great. I once climbed Mt. Fuji. It was tough, but it was a great experience! Now, when I see photos of it, I appreciate its beauty much more. Everybody should climb Mt. Fuji … but once is enough!

Step 1 Think of three good points about pictures.

Step 2 Write more than 70 words.
Use some of the useful expressions, if you like.

Pictures

Step 3 My Opinion

Step 4 After writing, share your ideas with your friends.

41

 # Shopping at Stores or Online

Shopping at Stores

 Why I think shopping at stores is better than shopping online.

 To my way of thinking, shopping at stores is better because you can touch the things you buy. You need to see the true colors and check out the quality, too.

 You can take your things home immediately. You do not have to wait for delivery.

 Window shopping is fun, too. You visit one store after another, and without spending money, you can imagine all the things you would buy.

 My Opinion

Personally, I prefer to shop at stores, too. I know exactly what I am getting. When you shop for clothes or shoes online, you are at risk of buying the wrong sizes and colors and it is troublesome to return them.

Step 1 Think of three good points about shopping online.

Step 2 Write more than 70 words.
Use some of the useful expressions, if you like.

Shopping Online

Step 3 My Opinion

Step 4 After writing, share your ideas with your friends.

20 Short Hair or Long Hair

Short Hair

 Short hair is better than long hair for three reasons.

 In my view, short hair is so much easier to take care of.

 It is more economical. You use less shampoo and conditioner. Having short hair makes it not only easy to save money, but also to save time.

 Short hair is especially great in summer! You look good and stay cool while people with long hair are hot and sweaty.

My Opinion

I used to have long hair, but I got tired of it. I love my short hair now. Once you try it, you will never go back to having long hair, trust me.

Step 1 Think of three good points about long hair.

Step 2 Write more than 70 words.
Use some of the useful expressions, if you like.

Long Hair

 Step 3 My Opinion

Step 4 After writing, share your ideas with your friends.

21 Showers or Baths

Showers

Lead Showers are better than baths. Here is why.

Reason 1 You do not need to wait to take a shower. Just turn on the hot water and jump in. Or, turn on the cold water if you want to shock yourself awake!

Reason 2 Showers are speedy. Most people can be in and out in five minutes and be sparkly clean. You are like a car at a car wash!

Reason 3 Showers are safer when you are tired. You are not likely to fall asleep in the shower.

 My Opinion

I like taking baths more than showers. They are more relaxing, especially just before going to bed. All my troubles melt away in the bathtub and I can sleep very well after that.

Step 1 Think of three good points about baths.

Step 2 Write more than 70 words.
Use some of the useful expressions, if you like.

<u>Baths</u>

 Step 3 My Opinion

Step 4 After writing, share your ideas with your friends.

22 Single-sex Schools or Co-ed Schools

  ## Single-sex Schools

Lead Single-sex schools are better than co-ed schools because …

Reason 1 First of all, in a single-sex school, it is probably easier to focus on your school activities and studies without the opposite sex around.

Reason 2 Usually, girls understand each other, and boys understand each other. At single-sex schools, both boys and girls can get along. They have more in common.

Reason 3 You can always meet opposite-sex friends outside of school in your free time. In fact, you will feel more excited because you do not see them every day in school.

 My Opinion

I have only attended co-ed schools. I think it was a good learning experience for me. When I was in elementary school, I thought boys were boring, but in high school, I discovered they were cool!

Step 1 Think of three good points about co-ed schools.

Step 2 Write more than 70 words.
Use some of the useful expressions, if you like.

Co-ed Schools

Step 3 My Opinion

Step 4 After writing, share your ideas with your friends.

23 Smart Friends or Good-looking Friends

Smart Friends

Lead Why smart friends may be better than good-looking friends.

Reason 1 In my opinion, it is better to have smart friends. They set a good example for you. You want to keep up with them, so you work harder. They challenge you to do your best.

Reason 2 Smart friends help you solve problems and you can learn from them. They help you with your homework or tests.

Reason 3 Your smart friends might invent something or do something important for society. You will be proud of having such famous friends.

My Opinion

I would say most of my friends are smarter than I am. But wait a minute! I must be smart after all because it is smart to have smart friends. My advice is to be smart and choose smart friends.

Step 1 Think of three good points about good-looking friends.

Step 2 Write more than 70 words.
Use some of the useful expressions, if you like.

Good-looking Friends

Step 3 My Opinion

Step 4 After writing, share your ideas with your friends.

24 Space Travel or Deep-sea Travel

Space Travel

 Why I think space travel is better than deep-sea travel.

 If you went to space, you could look down at the earth. It would give you a different point of view and all your troubles would disappear.

 In a spaceship, you could float in zero gravity. You could have such fun doing somersaults easily or eating floating popcorn—upside down!

 Traveling to space would be a fantastic adventure. One reason is that you never know who or what you might meet. I am confident I would enjoy talking to an alien.

 My Opinion

I would love to go to space. How wonderful it would be to float among the stars! I would stop at the moon first, and then I would head for Mars before coming back. Only if I decided to come back, that is.

Step 1 Think of three good points about deep-sea travel.

Step 2 Write more than 70 words.
Use some of the useful expressions, if you like.

Deep-sea Travel

Step 3 My Opinion

Step 4 After writing, share your ideas with your friends.

 # Spending Money or Saving Money

 ## Spending Money

 Lead Spending money is better than saving money for three reasons.

 Reason 1 You have to realize that spending money wisely is not wasting money. It is an investment in the future. It is good for a country's economy, too.

 Reason 2 Spending money on other people makes you happy, too. For instance, it is a pleasure to buy a present for someone you love, or treat a friend to coffee.

 Reason 3 The truth is, you only live once. And you never know what is going to happen tomorrow, so spend your money today!

 My Opinion

I love spending money. It is really hard for me to save it. My mother used to say that I had holes in my pockets because my money disappeared so quickly. But so what? I can always make more money!

Step 1 Think of three good points about saving money.

Step 2 Write more than 70 words.
Use some of the useful expressions, if you like.

Saving Money

 Step 3 My Opinion

Step 4 After writing, share your ideas with your friends.

26 Staying at a Hotel or Camping

Staying at a Hotel

 Staying at a hotel is better than camping. Here is why.

 As you know, when you arrive at the front desk, the receptionist will welcome you. You do not have to do anything but relax.

 In addition, you do not have to pack a lot of equipment such as a tent or a stove, just your suitcase.

 You can get a good rest in a hotel. You can sleep in a clean and comfortable bed. And you do not have to share your bed with insects or snakes.

My Opinion

It is really nice to stay in a good hotel. After I check in, I can take a bubble bath, order room service, and watch a movie. I feel like a queen!

56

Camping

Step 3 My Opinion

Step 4 After writing, share your ideas with your friends.

27 Sunsets or Sunrises

Sunsets

Lead Sunsets are better than sunrises because …

Reason 1 The sunset is a wonderful show of colors in the sky right in front of your eyes! Yellow turns to orange, red, purple, and then everything is black behind the shining moon and stars.

Reason 2 The sunset is a symbol of the end of the day. You can reflect on your day and look forward to the next one.

Reason 3 You do not have to get up early to watch the sunset. Just relax and enjoy the peaceful time.

 My Opinion

I prefer sunsets, too. For me, sunsets are so mysterious! I know the world is not flat, but as I watch the sun go down, I still wonder, where did it go?!

Step 1 Think of three good points about sunrises.

Step 2 Write more than 70 words.
Use some of the useful expressions, if you like.

Sunrises

Step 3 My Opinion

Step 4 After writing, share your ideas with your friends.

Traveling Abroad or in my Country

Traveling Abroad

Lead Why I think traveling abroad is better than traveling in my country.

Reason 1 I certainly know why people like traveling abroad. You hear other languages, see completely new sights, and taste very different food.

Reason 2 You can experience something dramatically unique such as riding an elephant in the jungle, or crossing the desert on a camel.

Reason 3 It is exciting to get a passport. Some people say that as they present it from country to country, it helps them develop a sense of identity as a citizen of their own country.

My Opinion

I like traveling abroad. When you take a long trip by plane, you can watch a couple of movies, read, play games, or take a nap. Then, suddenly, you wake up in a whole new world!

Step 1 Think of three good points about traveling in my country.

Step 2 Write more than 70 words.
Use some of the useful expressions, if you like.

Traveling in my Country

Step 3 My Opinion

Step 4 After writing, share your ideas with your friends.

 **Volunteer Work or Part-time Work**

  Volunteer Work

 Why volunteer work may be better than part-time work.

 When you volunteer, you gain valuable experience. Activities such as cleaning a riverbank, cooking for people in the community, or caring for animals, for instance, can teach you a lot.

 You can be a hero! You can help people, from little children to elderly people. They really appreciate it. And in exchange, it allows you to get great satisfaction.

 When you volunteer to work with foreigners, you help them, and at the same time, you can practice your English for free!

 My Opinion

I have done some volunteer work and really liked it. For example, I have picked up garbage in a park, welcomed travelers at our visitors' center, and sung songs for elderly people. I learned a lot from doing those things.

Step 1 Think of three good points about part-time work.
Step 2 Write more than 70 words.
Use some of the useful expressions, if you like.

Part-time Work

Step 3 My Opinion

Step 4 After writing, share your ideas with your friends.

 **Watching Movies at a Theater or at Home**

  ## Watching Movies at a Theater

Lead Why I think watching movies at a theater is better than watching movies at home.

Reason 1 As far as I am concerned, watching a movie at a theater is much better than watching one at home on a little TV screen, especially if it is a 3-D movie. It costs more, but it is worth it.

Reason 2 It is definitely thrilling to share the experience of an exciting movie with a crowd of people.

Reason 3 When you go into a theater, what is the first thing you smell? Popcorn! It is waiting there for you along with your candy and drink.

 My Opinion

Watching movies at a theater is real entertainment. In the dark, with the huge screen, and the sound surrounding me, I get completely lost in the story. I laugh, I cry, and I even clap when it is a happy ending!

Step 1 Think of three good points about watching movies at home.

Step 2 Write more than 70 words.
Use some of the useful expressions, if you like.

Watching Movies at Home

Step 3 My Opinion

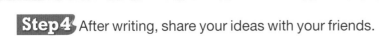

Step 4 After writing, share your ideas with your friends.

Series 1:TAGAKI ⑩ ~ ㊿

Teach Yourself

- Use sample sentences to write good English
- Think and write, then share your ideas
- Develop your interest with 30 x 5 textbooks=150 global topics
- Learn to write with structure: catchy sentences, facts, opinions, and punch lines
- Be independent learners. Evaluate yourself

TAGAKI ⑩	I can do it! Write and check it by yourself Learn to write three short sentences about 30 daily topics
TAGAKI ⑳	Choose your position: agree or disagree Learn to clearly express your feelings
TAGAKI ㉚	Pretend to be a third person and write Learn to write with structure: catchy sentences, facts, opinions, and punch lines
TAGAKI ㊵	Write two original sentences Learn to write about global topics
TAGAKI ㊿	Research a topic for additional facts and write about them State your opinion and make your own punch lines

TAGAKI Advanced 1 Three Reasons

First Published 2020
Eighth Published 2023
Writers: Suzy Nachtsheim, Yoko Matsuka
Contributors: Miyuki Kasuya, Rieko Kondo
English Proofreader: Glenn McDougall
Production: EDIT Co., Ltd.
Illustrator: Yumi Inaba
Designer: Taira Nakayama
DTP Designer: Taira Design
Record Producer: JAILHOUSE MUSIC Inc.
Narrators: Carolyn Miller, Howard Colefield, Peter von Gomm, Rumiko Varnes
Printer: Shinano Co., Ltd.

Special thanks to Chisato Mattox, Hiroko Sadano, Hiromi Sasaki, Kazuko Okazaki, Mie Nonaka, Mika Suzuki, Yuri Akamatsu, Chiemi, Mio, Nana, Riku, Taichi

Publisher: mpi Matsuka Phonics inc.
　　No.2 Koda Bldg 2F 2-16-2 Yoyogi,
　　Shibuya-ku, Tokyo 151-0053 Japan
　　fax:03-5302-1652
　　URL: https://www.mpi-j.co.jp

ISBN 978-4-89643-776-8
Printed in Japan

Download the audio files from the QR code or web page.
https://www.mpi-j.co.jp/contents/shop/mpi/contents/digital/tagaki_advanced_01.html